DAVID HADDEN

THE SONG BOOK

DAVID HADDEN

THE SONG BOOK

Kevin
Mayhew

We hope you enjoy the music in this book. Further copies are available
from your local music shop or Christian bookshop.

In case of difficulty, please contact the publisher direct by writing to:

The Sales Department
KEVIN MAYHEW LTD
Rattlesden
Bury St Edmunds
Suffolk
IP30 0SZ

Phone 01449 737978
Fax 01449 737834

Please ask for our complete catalogue of outstanding Church Music.

First published in Great Britain in 1997 by Kevin Mayhew Ltd.

© Copyright 1997 Kevin Mayhew Ltd.

ISBN 1 84003 079 8
ISMN M 57004 140 4
Catalogue No: 1450093

0 1 2 3 4 5 6 7 8 9

Front cover: *Profiles* by Diana Ong.
Reproduced by courtesy of Superstock Ltd, London.
Cover design by Jaquetta Sergeant

Music Editor: Donald Thomson
Music setting by Lynwen Davies and Daniel Kelly

Printed and bound in Great Britain by
Caligraving Limited Thetford Norfolk

Contents

About the Composer

DAVID HADDEN is the Director of Music for Covenant Ministries International. He is based at Leicester Christian Fellowship with his wife Ruth and their children, Faith, Samuel and Michael.

Over the years he has written many songs which have been sung by congregations all over the UK and abroad. Many have become favourites at the Dales and Wales Bible Weeks and the Grapevine Celebration.

He is the founder of the Trained and Skilled programme which aims to develop the skills of those who serve their local churches as vocalists and instrumentalists so that they are better able to flow with the Spirit of God as they worship.

My prayer is that through these songs you will be drawn closer to God, and find yourself able to use them personally and in your local church to worship the King.

DAVID HADDEN

1 A day of new beginnings

Text and Music: David Hadden

1. A day of new be-gin-nings. A fresh op-por-tu-ni-ty for those of us who ga-ther here in the pre-sence of our God. A new be-gin-ning for

2. A day of new be-gin-nings. A fresh op-por-tu-ni-ty for those who know the call of God deep with-in their hearts. A new be-gin-ning for

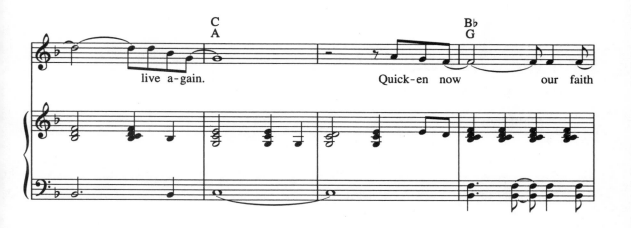

live a-gain. Quick-en now our faith

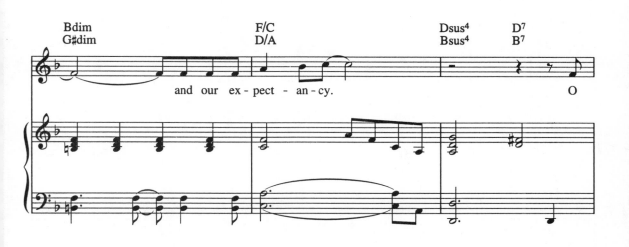

and our ex - pect - an-cy. O

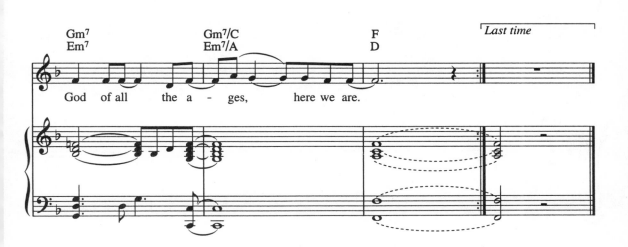

God of all the a - ges, here we are.

Last time

9

2 All the earth will be filled

Text and Music: David Hadden

2. From the north and south and east and west
   men and women all confess
   to the lordship of Jesus the Messiah.
   He is our friend, he is our King.
   A sacrifice of praise we bring
   as we acknowledge the glory of the Lord.

3 Better is one day

Text and Music: David Hadden

Better is one day in your courts, Lord, than a thou-sand some-where else. Better to be res-ting in your dwel-ling-place than be stri-ving by my-self. And

I would ra-ther be   a door - keep-er   in the house   of the Lord,   than to

dwell   in the tents   of   the wick-ed.

Bet-ter is   one   day   in your courts,   Lord,   than a

Last time

thou - sand   some-where else.

4 Day by day

Text and Music: David Hadden
arr. Chris Tambling

Day by day you be-stow your grace u-pon us,
each and ev-'ry mo-ment your eye is on this child.
Mer-cy flows, like a foun-tain filled with liv-ing wa-ter.
Com-pas-sion and for-give-ness, both are mine.

5 For a worldwide revival

Text: C.H. Morris adapted by David Hadden
Music: David Hadden arr. Chris Tambling

2. Send the showers of blessing
   as declared in your Word.
   Let the Spirit of promise
   on all flesh be outpoured.
   Send the latter rain on us,
   'till the land overflows;
   'till the desert rejoicing
   blossoms forth as the rose.
   Send the power, Lord . . .

3. News of nations awakening
   borne upon every breeze.
   And the Spirit of Jesus
   sends the church to its knees.
   For the prayers of his children
   God in mercy will own.
   The revival's beginning
   and the power's coming down.
   Send the power, Lord . . .

6 For unto us a child is born

Text: Isaiah 9: 6-7
Music: David Hadden

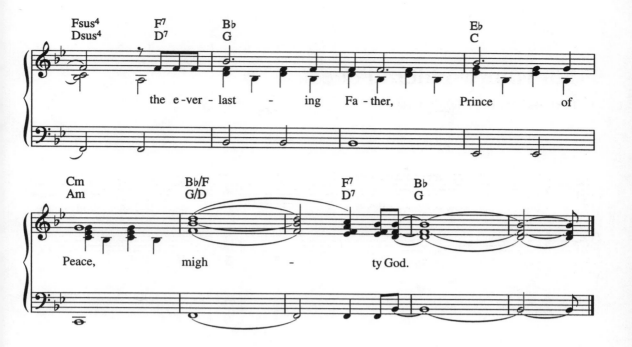

2. And there shall be no end
    to the increase of his rule,
    to the increase of his government and Peace.
    For he shall sit on David's throne
    upholding righteousness.
    Our God shall accomplish this.

3. For he is the mighty God,
    he is the Prince of Peace,
    the King of kings and Lord of lords.
    All honour to the King,
    all glory to his name,
    for now and evermore.

7 For your wonderful deeds

Text and Music: David Hadden

For your won-der-ful deeds, we give you thanks,

Lord, for your mar-vell-ous acts on be-half

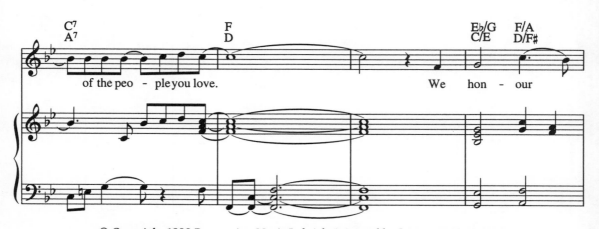

of the peo - ple you love. We hon - our

2. For your bountiful grace, we give you thanks, Lord,
   for the peace and the joy you bestow on the people you love.
   We honour you, we honour you,
   for your bountiful grace, we honour you.

8 From the North to the South

Text and Music: David Hadden
arr: Chris Mitchell

From the North to the South from the East to the West

we're going to see re-vi-val break-ing forth,

From the North see re-vi-val break-ing forth.

And we say to the North, give them up. And we say to the South,

9 He's given me a garment of praise

Text and Music: David Hadden

He's giv-en me a   gar-ment of praise
in-stead of a spi-rit of des-pair. He's gi-ven me a

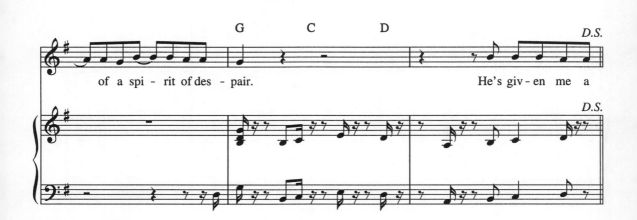

26

DAVID HADDEN

THE SONG BOOK

10 I join my heart with your heart *(You and I)*

Text and Music: David Hadden

11 It is you and you alone

Text and Music: David Hadden

It's not the joy, it's not the peace, it's you that must in - crease! It is you and you a -lone that sa - tis-fies my soul.

1. It is

2.

DAVID HADDEN

THE SONG BOOK

12 I will dwell

Text and Music: David Hadden

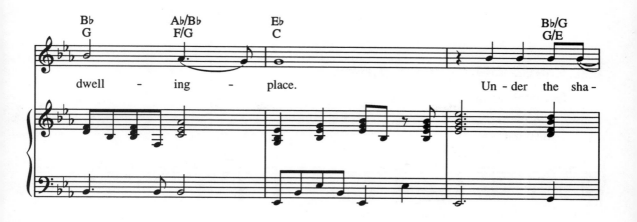

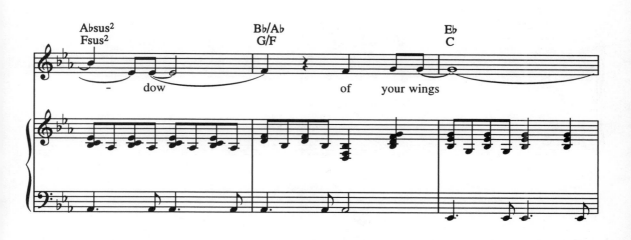

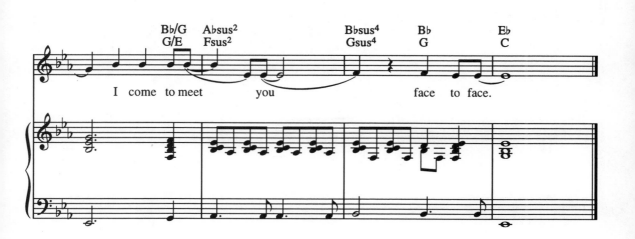

13 I will enter your gates

Text and Music: David Hadden

For you are good and your love en-dures for e-ver your faith-ful-ness through-out e-ter-ni-ty

Yes, you are good and I just love to dance and sing my praise to you, for you have made me glad,

O God.

To repeat

Last time

37

14 I will follow you *(El Shaddai)*

Text and Music: David Hadden
arr. Chris Tambling

15 Jesus, Jesus *(Hearts on fire)*

Text and Music: David Hadden
arr: Chris Tambling

Je - sus, (Je - sus,) Je - sus, (Je - sus.)

You have the name that's high - er than all o - ther names.

Je - sus, (Je - sus,) Je - sus, (Je - sus.)

You are the King, the migh - ty God, the one who reigns.

Glo - rious in splen - dour and ma - jes - ty,

clothed with the robe of au - tho - ri - ty,

Je - sus, my King, you will al - ways be

my deep - est joy, my one de - sire.

O Prince of Peace, you set my heart on fire,

To repeat

heart on fire.

41

16 Lord, we come before you now

Text and Music: David Hadden

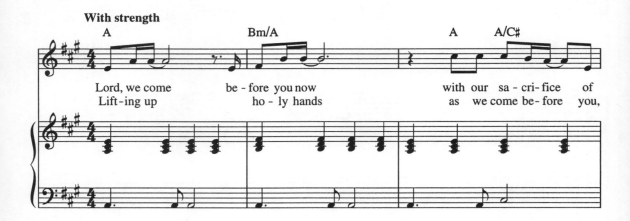

Lord, we come before you now
Lift-ing up ho-ly hands as we come be-fore you, with our sa-cri-fice of

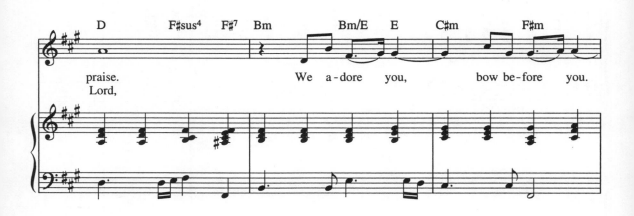

praise.
Lord,
We a-dore you, bow be-fore you.

In-hab-it our praise.

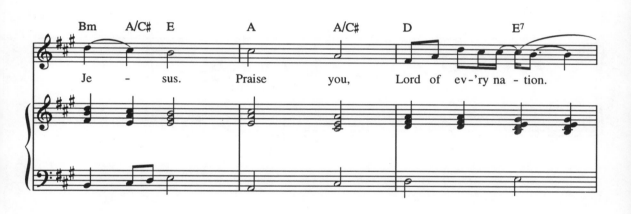

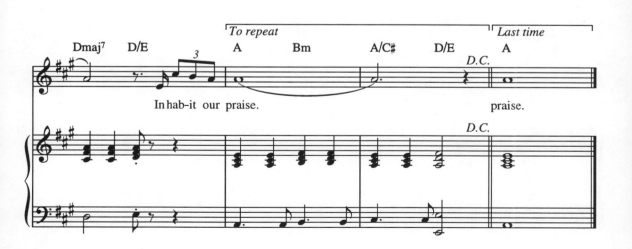

17 Lord, we come into your presence

Text and Music: David Hadden
arr. Chris Tambling

Lord, we come into your pre - sence.

Lord, we come to hon-our you.

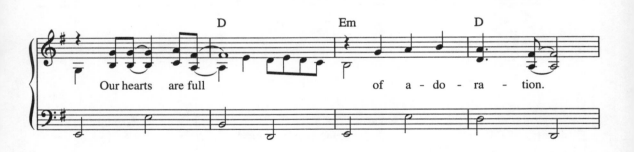

Our hearts are full of a - do - ra - tion.

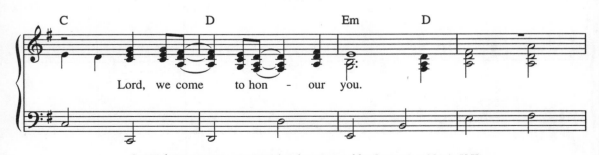

Lord, we come to hon - our you.

18 Living under the shadow of his wing

Text: Psalm 61:4
Music: David Hadden and Bob Silvester

Liv - ing un - der the sha-dow of his wing,

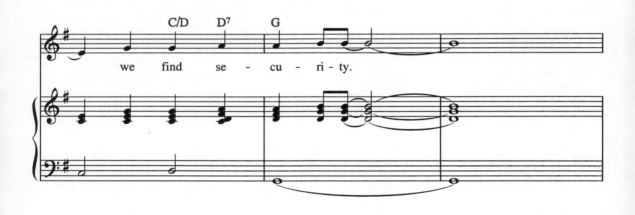

we find se - cu - ri - ty.

Stand - ing in his pre - sence, we will bring

our wor - ship, wor - ship, wor - ship to the King. King.

2. Bowed in adoration at his feet,
   we dwell in harmony.
   Voices joined together that repeat,
   worthy, worthy, worthy is the Lamb.

3. Heart to heart embracing in his love,
   reveals his purity.
   Soaring in my spirit like a dove,
   holy, holy, holy is the Lord.

DAVID HADDEN

THE SONG BOOK

19 One heart, one voice, one mind

Text and Music: David Hadden

One heart, one voice, one mind.

One in spi-rit, and one in love.

This will be the hope that we long for,

We're re - con - ciled, sin-ners now for-giv - en.

One in heart, and one in voice and mind.

20 Streams of worship

Text and Music: David Hadden

1. Streams of wor - ship and ri - vers of praise.
2. Thou - sands up - on thou - sands en - cir - cle the throne,
3. Streams of wor - ship and riv - vers of praise,

Asc - end - ing to the one who is the
sing - ing a new song to the
flow - ing from the lips of those who ne - ver

An - cient of Days. To him who is
one who is to come. To him who is
cease to be a - mazed. With him who is

DAVID HADDEN

THE SONG BOOK

21 The Lord is gracious

Text and Music: David Hadden

DAVID HADDEN

THE SONG BOOK

22 There's never been a time like this

Text and Music: David Hadden

1. There's ne-ver been a time like this for us to serve God's pur- pose. No time like the pre - sent to work the works of God.

2. Not on-ly are we cho - sen to serve our Fa - ther's pur- pose, to tell this ge-ne - ra - tion of the com-ing of our King:

3. In the mid-st of dark - ness the light of God a - ris- es, pro-claim - ing to the na-tions that Je - sus is the King.

A liv-ing de-mon-he's called us to be
He's cap-tured the af-

23 We are a chosen people

Text and Music: David Hadden

2. You have placed us into Zion
   in the new Jerusalem;
   thousand, thousand are their voices,
   singing to the Lamb.

24 We are the people

Text and Music: David Hadden

1. We are the peo - ple who've been pur-chased by the blood. And we en-joy wor - shipp-ing our God. As we de - clare God's great-ness, his ma - jes-ty and pow'r, we will

2. We declare to the pow'rs of this world,
   your time is now at hand.
   Our God has won a victory
   and we the church enjoy
   breaking down the pow'r of Satan in this land.

3. So arise all you people of the Lord,
   start living in the pow'r of God's word,
   for Satan is defeated
   and his hosts are on the run,
   as God's church moves in the pow'r of his Son.

stand u - ni - ted, ne -ver to be di - vi - ded, yes, we

stand to-ge-ther with our God.   2. We de-clare

To verses 2 & 3   *Last time*

D.S.

25 We know that all things work together
(We are more than conquerors)

Text and Music: David Hadden

Steady four

1. We know that all things work to-ge-ther for our good, for good to those who love the Lord. For God has called us to be just like his Son,

2. I am persuaded that neither death, nor life,
nor angels, principalities, nor powers,
nor things that are now, nor things that are to come,
can separate us from the love of Christ.

3. If God is for us, who against us can prevail?
No one can bring a charge against his chosen ones,
and there will be no separation from our Lord.
He has justified us through his precious blood.

to live and walk ac - cor - ding to his word.

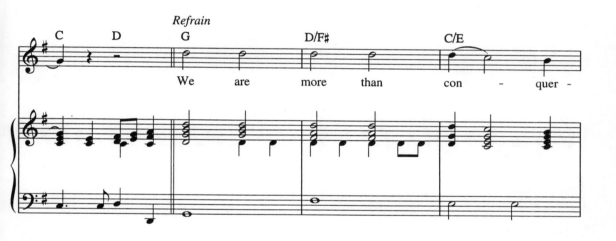

Refrain

We are more than con - quer -

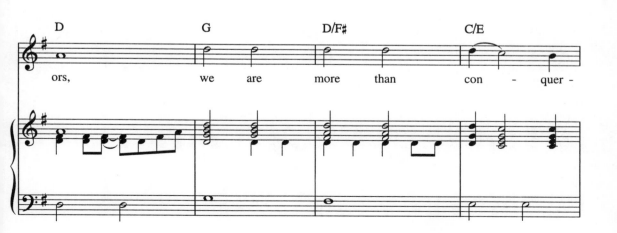

ors, we are more than con - quer -

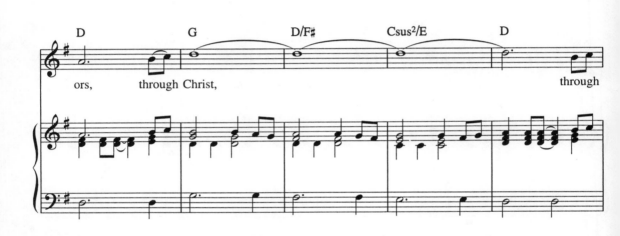